Where Do Monsters Live?

2 **A green monster lives in a green house.**

A red monster lives in a red house.

**A purple monster lives
in a purple house.**

A striped monster lives
in a striped house.

A spotted monster lives
in a spotted house.

An invisible monster lives
in an invisible house.

But an orange monster lives
under my bed!